This Book Belongs To ...